Level 1 • Book 2

Themes

Home, Sweet Home

I Am Brave

FLORIDA

Level 1
Book 2

Program Authors

Carl Bereiter

Andy Biemiller

Joe Campione

Iva Carruthers

Doug Fuchs

Lynn Fuchs

Steve Graham

Karen Harris

Jan Hirshberg

Anne McKeough

Peter Pannell

Michael Pressley

Marsha Roit

Marlene Scardamalia

Marcy Stein

Gerald H. Treadway Jr.

McGraw Hill **SRA**

Columbus, OH

Acknowledgments

Grateful acknowledgment is given to the following publishers and copyright owners for permissions granted to reprint selections from their publications. All possible care has been taken to trace ownership and secure permission for each selection included. In case of any errors or omissions, the Publisher will be pleased to make suitable acknowledgments in future editions.

Home, Sweet Home

HOMES by Abby Jackson © 2004 by Capstone Press. All rights reserved.
BUILDING A HOUSE COPYRIGHT © 1981 BY BYRON BARTON. Illustrations copyright © 1981 BYRON BARTON. Used by permission of HarperCollins Publishers.
From: THE WHITE HOUSE by Lloyd G. Douglas. Copyright © 2003 by Rosen Book Works, Inc.
From ALWAYS WONDERING by Aileen Fisher. Copyright © 1991 Aileen Fisher. Used by permission of Marian Reiner on behalf of the Boulder Public Library Foundation, Inc.
PATTERNS OF LIFE: FINDING SHELTER by Daphne Butler. Reproduced by permission of Hodder and Stoughton Limited.
"Home" from THE BIG BOOK OF CLASSROOM POEMS by Kathleen M. Hollenbeck. Published by Teaching Resources/Scholastic Inc. Copyright © 2004 by Kathleen M. Hollenbeck. Reproduced by permission.
THIS HOUSE IS MADE OF MUD. Text copyright © 1991 by Ken Buchanan. Illustrations copyright © 1991 by Libba Tracy. Reprinted by permission of Northland Publishing, LLC.

I Am Brave

MY BROTHER IS AFRAID OF JUST ABOUT EVERYTHING by Lois Osborn. Copyright (c) 1982. Reprinted by permission of Browne & Miller Literary Associates, Chicago, IL.
THERE'S A BIG, BEAUTIFUL WORLD OUT THERE! By Nancy Carlson. Copyright © 2002 Nancy Carlson. All rights reserved including the right of reproduction in whole or in part in any form. This edition published by arrangement with Viking Children's Books, a member of Penguin Young Readers Group, a division of Penguin Group (USA) Inc.
"Night Comes" From A BUNCH OF POEMS AND VERSES by Beatrice Schenk de Regniers. Copyright © 1977 by Beatrice Schenk de Regniers. Used by permission of Marian Reiner. Illustration by Emma Shaw-Smith. Used by permission of Barefoot Books.
CLYDE MONSTER by Robert Crowe and illustrated by Kay Chorao. Text copyright © 1976 by Robert Crowe, 1976. Illustrations copyright © Kay Chorao, 1976. All rights reserved including the right of reproduction in whole or in part in any form. This edition published by arrangement with Dutton Children's Books, a member of Penguin Young Readers Group, a division of Penguin Group (USA) Inc.
IRA SLEEPS OVER by Bernard Waber. Copyright © 1972 by Bernard Waber. Reprinted by permission of Houghton Mifflin Company. All rights reserved.

Photo Credits

vi (tr) © Peter Beck/CORBIS; vi (cl) © Wolfgang Kaehler/CORBIS; vii (tr) © Dennis O'Clair/Getty Images, Inc.; vii (cr) © Stephen Dalton/NHPA Ltd.; 10–11 © Gavin Hellier/Getty Images, Inc.; 14–15 © Lester Lefkowitz/CORBIS; 16 © Dick Luria/Getty Images, Inc.; 17 © Ariel Skelley/CORBIS; 18 © Peter Beck/CORBIS; 19 © PhotoDisc/Getty Images, Inc.; 20 © Caroline von Tuempling/Getty Images, Inc.; 21 © Johner/Getty Images, Inc.; 22 © Peter Turnley/CORBIS; 23 © Steve Vidler/SuperStock; 25 © Grayce Roessler/Index Stock Imagery, Inc.; 26 © Bruno Morandi/Getty Images, Inc.; 24 © Lester Lefkowitz/CORBIS; 27 © Kevin Fleming/CORBIS; 28 © Scott Christopher/Index Stock Imagery, Inc.; 29 © Blend Images/Getty Images, Inc.; 30 (inset) © Lester Lefkowitz/CORBIS, (bkgd) © Grayce Roessler/Index Stock Imagery, Inc.; 31 © Peter Beck/CORBIS; 32–33 © Digital Vision/Getty Images, Inc.; 33 (l) © Mark Chappell/Animals Animals/Earth Scenes, (r) © Kennan Ward/CORBIS; 36–37 © Diana Frances Jones; Gallo Images/CORBIS; 38 (t) © Wayne Walton/Getty Images, Inc., (bl) © Nicholas DeVore/Tony Stone Images, (br) © Blair Seitz/Photo Researchers, Inc.; 39 (tl) © Wolfgang Kaehler/Corbis, (br) © Focus/Moller/Woodfin Camp & Associates; 40 (tl) © Craig Aurness/CORBIS, (tr) © Peter Adams/Getty Images, Inc., (br) © Dietrich Rose/zefa/CORBIS; 41 (t) © Digital Vision/Getty Images, Inc., (br) © Momatiuk/Eastcott/Woodfin Camp & Associates; 42 (t) © José Fuste Rage/zefa/CORBIS, (b) © Karen Beattie/Alamy; 43 (t) © Craig Aurness/Woodfin Camp & Associates, (br) © David Hiser/Tony Stone Images; 44 (t) © Hilarie Kavanagh/Tony Stone Images, (b) © Macduff Everton/CORBIS; 45 (l) Paul Chesley/National Geographic Society Image Collection, (r) ©Tony Arruza/CORBIS; 46 (t) © Wolfgang Kaehler/CORBIS, (b) © Kevin Fleming/CORBIS; 47 (t) © Chad Ehlers/Alamy, (b) ©Sylvain Grandadam/Getty Images, Inc.; 48 (t) E G Company; 48–49 (bkgd) © Wayne Walton/Getty Images, Inc., 58 courtesy of Bound to Stay Books, Inc.; 64–65 (bkgd) © Dennis O'Clair/Getty Images, Inc.; 66 © Royalty-Free/CORBIS; 67 © Brooks Kraft/CORBIS; 68 (t) © Alan Schein Photography/CORBIS, © PhotoDisc/Getty Images, Inc.; 69 © Stanley Tretick/Sygma/CORBIS; 70, 71 © Bettmann/CORBIS; 72 White House Historical Association; 73 © Wally McNamee/CORBIS; 74 © Lake County Museum/CORBIS; 75 © AFP/Getty Images, Inc.; 76 © Stock Connection Distribution/Alamy; 77 © Lester Lefkowitz/CORBIS; 78–79 © PhotoDisc/Getty Images, Inc.; 86 © Creatas/PunchStock; 87 © PhotoDisc/Getty Images, Inc.; 88–89 © Stephen Dalton/NHPA Ltd.; 90 © Adrienne Gibson/Animals Animals/Earth Scenes; 91 © Michael S. Bisceglie/Animals Animals/Earth Scenes; 92 © Kit Houghton/CORBIS; 93 © Frank Lukasseck/zefa/CORBIS; 94 © Stephen Dalton/NHPA Ltd.; 95 © Paul Nicklen/National Geographic Society, Image Collection; 96 © Martin Harvey/NHPA Ltd.; 97 © Paul A. Souders/CORBIS; 98 © Zigmund Leszczynski/Animals Animals/Earth Scenes; 99 (tl) © Roger Tidman/NHPA/Photoshot, (tr, b) © W. Perry Conway/CORBIS; 100 © Ute & Juergen Schimmelpfenning/zefa/CORBIS; 101 © George Bernard/Animals Animals/Earth Scenes; 102 (cr) © Jeff Bergdoll/Animal Animals/Earth Scenes, (bl) © Hal Beral/CORBIS; 103 (tr) © Anthony Bannister/NHPA Ltd., (cl) © Dietrich Rose/zefa/CORBIS; 104 © Lance Nelson/Stock Photos/zefa/CORBIS; 105 © Felix St Clair Renard/Getty Images, Inc.; 106 (cl) © W. Perry Conway/CORBIS, (bc) © Felix St Clair Renard/Getty Images, Inc., (br) © Hal Beral/CORBIS; 136 (t) courtesy of Ken Buchanan, (b) courtesy of Libbra Tracy; 172 (t) Lois Osborn; 172 (b) courtesy of Erica Villnave; 174–175 © Digital Vision/Getty Images, Inc.; 175 © Michael Newman/PhotoEdit; 198 courtesy of Nancy Carlson; 222 (t) © Merle Fox Photography; 222 (b) Kay Chorao; 230 (t) © Scala/Art Resource, NY, (b) courtesy of Gene Barretta; 266 courtesy of Bernard Waber; 268–269 © OSF/Stan Osolinski/Animals Animals/Earth Scenes; 269 © Robert Brenner/PhotoEdit.

SRAonline.com

 SRA

Send all inquiries to this address:
SRA/McGraw-Hill
4400 Easton Commons
Columbus, OH 43219-6188

ISBN: 978-0-07-609651-0
MHID: 0-07-609651-3

2 3 4 5 6 7 8 9 RRW 13 12 11 10 09 08 07

Program Authors

Carl Bereiter, Ph.D.
University of Toronto

Andy Biemiller, Ph.D.
University of Toronto

Joe Campione, Ph.D.
University of California, Berkeley

Iva Carruthers, Ph.D.
Northeastern Illinois University

Doug Fuchs, Ph.D.
Vanderbilt University

Lynn Fuchs, Ph.D.
Vanderbilt University

Steve Graham, Ed.D.
Vanderbilt University

Karen Harris, Ed.D.
Vanderbilt University

Jan Hirshberg, Ed.D.
Reading Specialist

Anne McKeough, Ph.D.
University of Toronto

Peter Pannell
Principal, Longfellow Elementary School,
Pasadena, California

Michael Pressley, Ph.D.
Michigan State University

Marsha Roit, Ed.D.
National Reading Consultant

Marlene Scardamalia, Ph.D.
University of Toronto

Marcy Stein, Ph.D.
University of Washington, Tacoma

Gerald H. Treadway, Jr., Ed.D.
San Diego State University

Unit 9 Table of Contents

Home, Sweet Home

Unit 10 Table of Contents

I Am Brave

Home, Sweet Home

Throughout the world, animals and people make homes from materials they find. Are all homes alike? What makes a good home for all the different people and animals in the world?

Theme Connection

Look at the photo of colorful houses on Chiappini Street, Bo Kaap, Muslim-Cape Malay area, Cape Town, South Africa, Africa. What is different about the homes in this photo?

BIG Idea

Why are homes important?

Read the article to find the meanings of these words, which are also in "Homes":

✦ packed
✦ clay
✦ roof
✦ sturdy

Vocabulary Strategy

Word Structure can help you find the meaning of *packed*.

Vocabulary

Warm-Up

Steve packed his suitcase. He placed the clay dog he had made at school in the middle. "I hope it will be safe with all these clothes around it," he said.

"I think it will," said his mother. "It is a simple way to keep it safe.

"The woven napkins you made are at hand too," she said. "I will pack them in the last box."

Moving Truck

Steve was happy his family was moving. His house was old and needed a lot of repairs. Steve's new house had a new roof. It was made of bricks.

"Our new house will be as sturdy as a rock!" Steve joked.

"It will be the best house we have ever had!" said his father.

GAME

Memory Game Write each vocabulary word on an index card. Then write each word's meaning on its own card. Turn over, and spread out the cards. Take turns with a partner, matching each word and its meaning.

Concept Vocabulary

The concept word for this lesson is *material.* Material is what things are made from. Wood is a material for building houses. Houses are made of different materials. What other materials are used for building houses?

Genre

Informational Writing informs or explains something real.

Comprehension Strategy

 Asking Questions

As you read, ask yourself questions to help you better understand the selection.

14

Homes

by Abby Jackson

Focus Question

Why are houses made of different materials?

What Is a Home?

What is a home? A home is the place where we live. It is a place where we feel safe.

It is a place to return to at the end
of the day. A home is a place to cook,
eat, and sleep.

A home gives us shelter. Its walls keep in heat. Its roof keeps out rain and snow.

All of these things make a home.
But homes do not look the same
everywhere.

Using What Is at Hand

There are many kinds of homes. People make their homes from what is at hand.

This home is made of wood. Wood is easy to build with.

This home is made of sticks
and packed mud. Mud makes a
sturdy house.

This home has a roof made of grass. The grass is woven tightly to keep out rain.

This home is in the desert. It is made
of baked clay. The clay keeps the
house cool.

This home is in the Arctic. It is made from blocks of ice and snow. Yet people stay warm inside.

Homes on the Move

Some people are always moving
from place to place. They build simple
homes wherever they go.

They can build their homes quickly.
These homes are simple but sturdy.

Some of these homes are made of sticks and branches. Others are made of blankets.

These homes keep people safe from wind and sand. They are also easy to pick up and move.

Your Home

People live in different kinds of homes. What is your home like?

Meet the Author

Abby Jackson

Abby Jackson is a pseudonym, or made-up name, for the author of "Homes." Some authors use made-up names to hide their identities.

Home, Sweet Home

Theme Connections

Within the Selection

1. Where do you live if your house is made of ice and snow?

2. Where do you live if your house is made of clay?

Beyond the Selection

3. If you were to build a home, what materials would you use?

4. How would you decorate your home?

Write about It!

Describe what kind of home you would like to have when you grow up.

Remember to look for pictures of homes to add to the **Concept/ Question Board**.

Strong Homes

Warm Homes

People who live in cold areas need homes to stay warm. Some people use igloos for shelter.

Sturdy Homes

People make their homes sturdy. They build them to keep out rain, snow, ice, and heat. Wood, bricks, and stones make strong homes.

Animal Homes

Animals need good homes too. The kangaroo rat is a desert animal. It lives in a burrow under the ground. The burrow is a shelter that keeps desert animals cool during the day.

Polar bears are arctic animals. They make snowy dens for shelter.

1. How are the headings helpful?

2. How are animal and people homes alike? How are they different?

3. Why do you think some animals hibernate in the winter?

Try It!

As you continue your investigations, list any questions you have about homes.

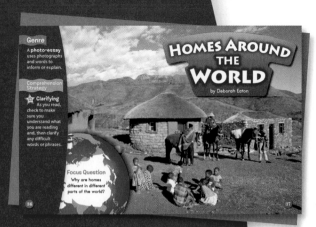

HOMES AROUND THE WORLD
by Deborah Eaton

Read the article to find the meanings of these words, which are also in "Homes Around the World" or "Building a House":

✦ porch
✦ cement
✦ electrician
✦ hut

Vocabulary Strategy

Context Clues can help you find the meanings of *porch* and *hut*.

Vocabulary

Warm-Up

Gabe's dad started to unfold a piece of paper. "This is where our new house will be," he said. "Our house will be south of the apartments. It will have a big porch. It will have a tin roof."

A loud sound made Gabe look away from the map. He saw a bulldozer moving dirt. "A house will be there soon," Gabe's dad said.

Gabe's dad explained that the map was a plan. "Do they plan the cement basements?" asked Gabe. Gabe's dad nodded.

"An electrician has a map of each house. Electricians know where to put the wires. The carpenters know where to hammer nails. Sometimes they keep their tools in a hut."

Gabe got out his own paper. He began to draw. "I am drawing how I want my room to look!" he said.

Illustrate It Pretend you are mapping a fort for your playground. Write a sentence using each vocabulary word.

Concept Vocabulary

The concept word for this lesson is *process.* A process is a series of actions. These actions help you get what you want. Why is building a house such a long process? Why is painting at the end of the process?

A **photo-essay** uses photographs and words to inform or explain.

Comprehension Strategy

⭐ **Clarifying**
As you read, check to make sure you understand what you are reading, and then clarify any difficult words or phrases.

Focus Question

Why are homes different in different parts of the world?

HOMES AROUND THE WORLD

by Deborah Eaton

Here you will see many homes
and many faces in many different
far-off places.

Argentina

Lesotho, South Africa

The Philippines

Mali

Cliff houses are cool
when the sun is hot.

Germany

It's not too hot here. Grass grows
on a roof.

A reed hut is made of dried plants.

Peru

You need a ladder to get to some pueblo houses.

New Mexico, USA

Austria

Flowers make this home pretty.

Their house is up on stilts.

The Philippines

Poland

His house has a
tin roof.

Trailers are homes on wheels.

Utah, USA

Kerala, India

Some homes float.

Some homes fold right up.

Morocco

People can even turn
palm leaves into a home.

Guatemala

A porch is a nice place to sit.

Thailand

A fireplace
warms a home.

Taos Pueblo, New Mexico, USA

44

China

Doors are for
friends coming in.

Windows let light
in and let people
smile out.

West Indies

45

Big and tall . . .

Indonesia

Somalia

round and small . . .

all over the world, homes are
for living . . .

Zimbabwe

Utah, USA

and homes are for enjoying.

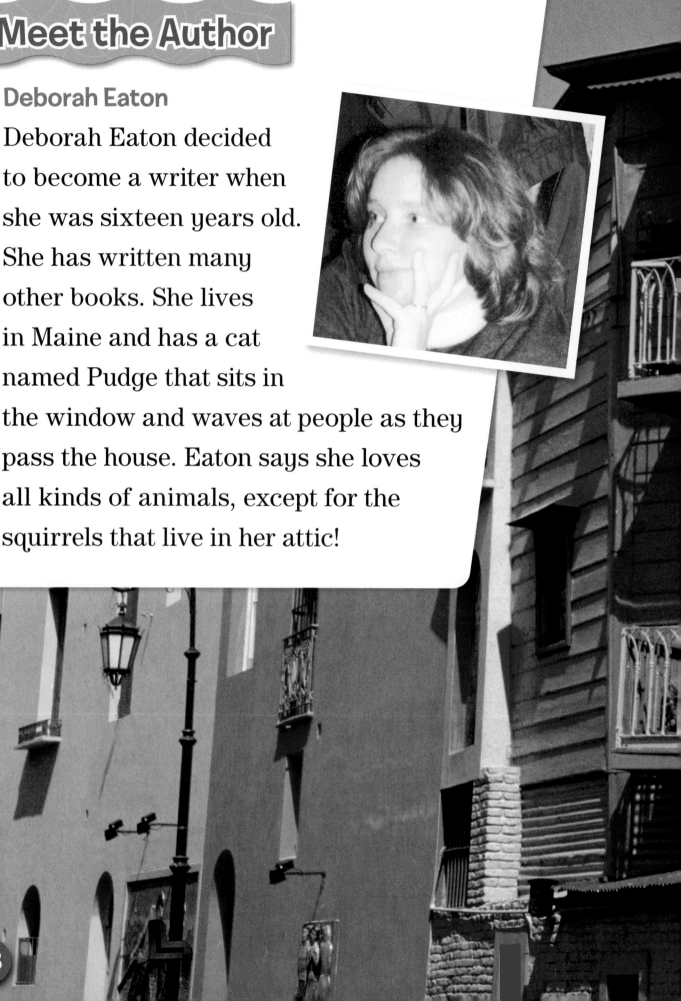

Meet the Author

Deborah Eaton

Deborah Eaton decided to become a writer when she was sixteen years old. She has written many other books. She lives in Maine and has a cat named Pudge that sits in the window and waves at people as they pass the house. Eaton says she loves all kinds of animals, except for the squirrels that live in her attic!

Home, Sweet Home

Theme Connections

Within the Selection

1. What kind of home has wheels?

2. What kind of home can float?

Across Selections

3. How are the homes in "Homes Around the World" similar to the homes in "Homes"?

Beyond the Selection

4. What could you do to make a house look pretty outside?

Write about It!

Describe the kinds of materials you could use to build a house.

Remember to look for pictures of homes to add to the **Concept/ Question Board**.

Comprehension Skill

☆ **Classify and Categorize** As you read, group together things and ideas that are alike.

Building a HOUSE

written and illustrated by Byron Barton

Focus Questions

What kinds of workers help build a house? What things do people use to build a house?

On a green hill a bulldozer
digs a big hole.

Builders hammer and saw.

A cement mixer pours cement.

Bricklayers lay large white blocks.

Carpenters come and make a wooden floor.

They put up walls.

They build a roof.

A bricklayer builds a fireplace and a chimney too.

A plumber puts in pipes for water.

An electrician wires for electric lights.

Carpenters put in windows and doors.

Painters paint inside and out.

The workers leave.

The house is built.

The family
moves inside.

57

Meet the Author and Illustrator

Byron Barton

Byron Barton became known as "the artist" in grade school. He got the name because he often painted pictures. He said, "My pictures were hanging all over the back walls of the class." He grew up to write and illustrate stories about how to do things like build a house, put together dinosaur bones, and travel on a spaceship.

58

Home, Sweet Home
Theme Connections

Within the Selection

1. Why does it take so many people to build a house?

2. Why must you build a house in a special order?

Across Selections

3. Would the steps in "Building a House" be used for all the houses in "Homes Around the World"? Why or why not?

Beyond the Selection

4. If you were building a house, which job would you enjoy?

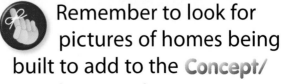

Remember to look for pictures of homes being built to add to the **Concept/ Question Board.**

Social Studies Inquiry

Then and Now

Genre

Expository Text contains facts about real people and events.

Feature

Headings tell you what a paragraph will be about.

Long Ago

Long ago, people lived on farms. They grew their food. They raised animals to help them.

Their homes did not have electricity. They got heat from fireplaces. Life was not easy.

Now

Today's farms are different. Farmers still grow food. They still raise animals. Machines help farmers work. They make farmers' jobs easier.

City Life

Some people live in the city. Some people live in houses with a porch.

Homes can be big or small. Homes keep us safe.

1. How do you know that the first paragraph and the second paragraph are about different time periods?

2. Why might someone think it is easier to live on a farm now?

3. How do homes keep us safe?

Try It!

Draw a picture of how farm life was long ago. Write a sentence about it.

Informational **Writing** informs or explains something real.

Comprehension Skill

★ **Main Idea and Details** Identify the main idea and details of the selection.

The White House

Focus Question

Why is the White House important?

by Lloyd G. Douglas

Read the article to find the meanings of these words, which are also in "The White House" or "Snail's Pace ":

✦ trudge
✦ president
✦ famous

Vocabulary Strategy

Context Clues in the text help you find the meanings of words. Use context clues to determine the meanings of *trudge* and *president.*

62

Vocabulary

Warm-Up

I heard my brother trudge down the steps. He doesn't know it is a special day or that we are going to the White House.

"Come on!" I say. "We are going to see the White House!"

"What is so neat about the White House?" Ben asks. "We have seen lots of houses."

Ben is only four years old. If he were older, he would probably know more about it.

"The president of the United States lives in the White House," I tell Ben. "He's the leader of our country!"

"Is he famous?" Ben asks.

"Everybody knows him!" I reply.

"Maybe if I go to the White House I will get to know him too," Ben said.

GAME

Write about It! Read the selection vocabulary words. Use each word to make a sentence about a parade. Share your sentences with your class.

Concept Vocabulary

The concept word for this lesson is *lead.* To lead sometimes means "to be in charge of others." Your teacher leads your class. The president leads our country. Can you think of anyone else who leads? Explain your answer.

Genre

Informational Writing informs or explains something real.

Comprehension Skill

⭐ **Main Idea and Details**
Identify the main idea and details of the selection.

Focus Question

Why is the White House important?

The White House

by Lloyd G. Douglas

The White House has been a symbol of America for more than two hundred years.

The president of the United States lives in the White House with his family.

The address of the White House is 1600 Pennsylvania Avenue. It is in Washington, D.C.

Many presidents have lived in the White House.

John Adams was the first president to
live in the White House.

He was the second president of the United States.

The White House has many rooms.

The president works in a room called the Oval Office.

The East Room is the largest room in the White House.

Many parties and dinners have been held there.

People can visit some parts of the White House.

Many people visit the White House every year.

The White House is the most famous home in America.

It is an important American symbol.

77

Meet the Author

Lloyd G. Douglas

Lloyd G. Douglas has written many selections. In his selections, he teaches children a lot about the United States. He has written books about the White House, the Statue of Liberty, the Pledge of Allegiance, and the American flag. Douglas writes books to help children understand more about themselves and the world around them.

Theme Connections

Within the Selection

1. What is the address of the White House?

2. Who was the first president to live in the White House?

Across Selections

3. How is the White House different from other homes you have learned about in this unit?

Beyond the Selection

4. How is the White House a symbol?

Write about It!

Describe a room in the White House. Write a sentence about it.

Remember to look for articles about the White House to add to the **Concept/Question Board.**

Poetry is a special kind of writing in which sounds and meanings of words are combined to create ideas and feelings.

Comprehension Strategy

⭐ **Visualizing** As you read, picture in your mind what is happening in the selection.

Focus Question

What is the purpose of a snail's shell?

Snail's Pace

by Aileen Fisher

illustrated by Pete Whitehead

81

Maybe it's so

that snails are slow.

They trudge along and tarry.

But isn't it true

you'd slow up, too,

if you had a house to carry?

Vote for the President!

There are rules for people who want to be president. First they must be born in the United States. They must be at least thirty-five years old. The president must also be a citizen of our country.

People who want to be president make speeches. They talk to the press. They want people to vote for them.

Presidents are elected. A president's job lasts for four years. Then there is another vote. Sometimes the president keeps his job. Other times someone else wins the vote. Members of our country vote for the leader. When you are eighteen years old, you can vote too.

Think Link

1. What is the sequence of events in the first paragraph?

2. How long does a president keep the job?

3. Who votes for the president? Why do you think it is important to vote?

Try It!

List any questions you have about the White House.

Read the article to find the meanings of these words, which are also in "Finding Shelter" or "Home":

+ creatures
+ hibernating
+ comfort
+ shady

Vocabulary Strategy

Context Clues in the text help you find the meanings of words. Use context clues to determine the meanings of *comfort* and *shady*.

Vocabulary

Warm-Up

Many creatures spend the winter hibernating. Bears sleep in dens. Bears use leaves and plants to build comfort in their shady dens.

Female bears have babies in the winter. The babies are called cubs. Bears stay with their mothers for more than a year.

Bears eat things they can reach. They like berries and acorns. Sometimes they eat trash. They also like nuts and insects. Bears can get really big.

Bears are good swimmers. They move around in the morning and at night. Bears have strong legs. Most bears are good tree climbers.

GAME

Sentence Building
Work with a partner to create sentences using the vocabulary words from the list.

Concept Vocabulary

The concept word for this lesson is **dwelling**. A dwelling is a home. People live in many different dwellings. Some people live in houses. Others live in apartments. Can you think of any animal dwellings?

Genre

Informational Writing informs or explains something real.

Comprehension Skill

☆ **Compare and Contrast**
As you read, compare and contrast ideas, characters, and events.

Finding

Focus Question

Where do animals live?

Shelter

by Daphne Butler

Whatever the Weather

What's the weather like where you live? Is it cold sometimes or rainy? Or is it very hot?

Almost all creatures, all over the world, need somewhere to shelter. Many must find shelter from the weather.

Warm Coats

Different animals have different
ways of living with the weather.

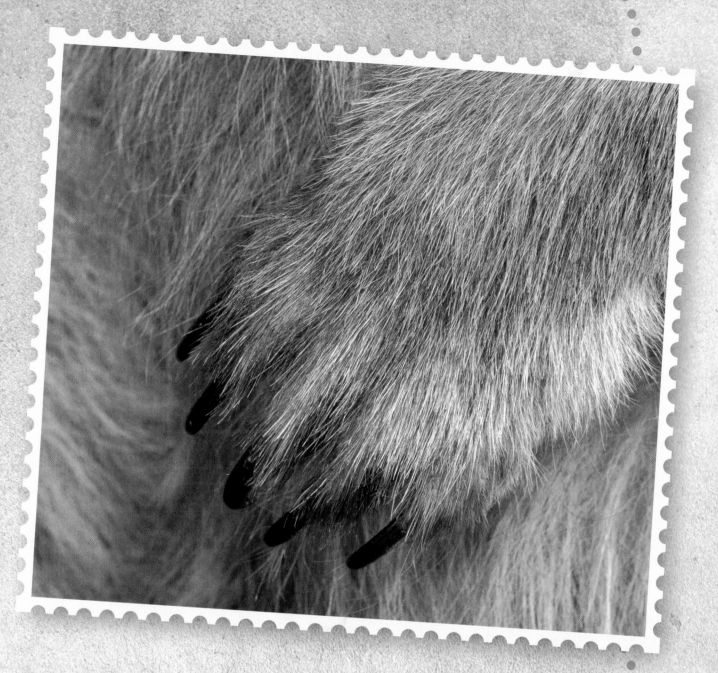

Some grow a thick hairy coat in autumn. This traps air, keeping their skin warm and dry.

The extra hair falls out in the spring. This leaves only a thin coat for the hot summer.

Sleeping until Spring

Some animals find a safe place to sleep in autumn. They stay there all winter, hibernating until spring. Then the weather warms up again.

Fish lie quietly on the bottom of
lakes and rivers. In the cold water
under ice, they wait for the thaw.

Shady Places

Animals in hot countries do not need thick coats. They need shady places. These shady covers protect them from the heat of the sun.

Some climb high in the leafy branches. Here they might find a cool breeze, too.

Safe Places

Animals also need safe places to hide from their enemies. This is a place their babies can stay until they are strong.

Holes in the Ground

Some animals dig themselves holes
in the ground. It is safe underground
and cool in summer, too.

A hole is a safe place to hibernate.
It keeps away the winter weather.

Nest Building

Some animals build nests.

Birds collect twigs, grass, or moss. Wasps and hornets make theirs with walls like paper.

How do you think spiders build their nests?

What kind of animals make strange-looking hills?

Building Houses

People also build nests to live in. They build houses with strong walls and roofs. Their houses are warm and dry in winter. They stay cool and shady in summer.

Living Anywhere

All animals, even people, learn how
to live in the area around them.

People can also travel to any part
of the world. They can change their
clothes and their houses to go with
the weather.

Daphne Butler

Writing about all kinds of topics is Daphne Butler's specialty. She writes books to introduce students to interesting topics. She has written books about nature, the forest, and various animals. She has also written about places and objects, such as a hospital and wind.

Home, Sweet Home

Theme Connections

Within the Selection

1. How do some animals stay warm in the winter?

2. Why do animals live in different kinds of homes?

Across Selections

3. How are animals' homes like the homes people live in?

Beyond the Selection

4. Think about animals that are not in the selection. What are their homes like?

Write about It!

Why do animals and people need shelter?

Remember to look for pictures of animal homes to add to the **Concept/ Question Board.**

Genre

Poetry is a special kind of writing in which sounds and meanings of words are combined to create ideas and feelings.

Comprehension Strategy

☆ **Making Connections**

As you read, make connections between what you know and what you are reading.

Focus Question

What do you think makes a good home?

Home

from *The Big Book of Classroom Poems*

by Kathleen M. Hollenbeck

illustrated by Todd Bonita

Home is more than

a bedroom and kitchen,

a place for your toothbrush,

a room with TV.

More than just shelter

from cold rainy weather,

home is a place

where you find family.

Home is a feeling,

a place of belonging.

No one can say

one is better or best.

Home is the place that your

heart wants to go to

when you need comfort,

or laughter,

or rest.

Science Inquiry

The Hope Town News
Animals Get a Drink
by Mary Myers

Some local people saw why lots of creatures live near Lake Hope.

"I have never seen so many deer in my life," said Roger Hand. "They were just to the right of the trees."

Susan Hand was just as excited. "We saw some raccoons under a bush," she said. "We even saw a turtle next to the lake. The hot day must have made the animals thirsty."

The Hands plan to come back to Lake Hope soon. "I hope we will see more animals!" said Mary Hand.

Perhaps that is why the lake is called Lake Hope.

Think Link

1. What animal is to the right of the trees?

2. What place is this article about?

3. How can you tell what is said by Susan Hand?

Try It!

Look at a newspaper. Circle the quotes in one of the articles.

113

Read the article to find the meanings of these words, which are also in "This House Is Made of Mud":

✦ tunnels
✦ share

Vocabulary Strategy

Word Structure can help you find the meaning of *share*.

Vocabulary

Warm-Up

Moles live in different areas. Some moles live in tunnels underground. Moles rarely share the same space.

Moles eat mostly worms and insects. They look a lot like mice or shrews. Moles have big front feet.

Moles spend almost all their lives in tunnels. Their feet are very helpful. They can use them to make their tunnels longer and longer.

Young moles are born in nests. The babies are usually born in April. The baby moles stay in their nests for five weeks.

Moles have small eyes. Their eyes are hidden beneath their fur, so they do not get dirt in their eyes when they dig tunnels.

GAME

Sentence Building
Work with a partner to create sentences using the vocabulary words. Choose a word from the list, and challenge your partner to make up a sentence using the word.

Concept Vocabulary

The concept word for this lesson is *divide*. To divide is to share a part of something. Sometimes we divide food. Other times we divide space. Can you think of something you have had to divide in your home?

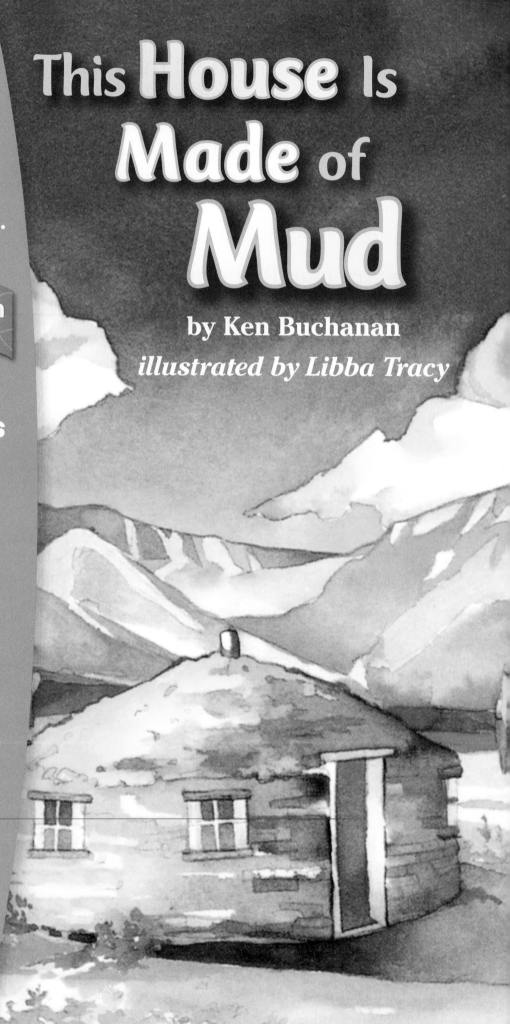

This House Is Made of Mud

by Ken Buchanan

illustrated by Libba Tracy

116

Esta casa está hecha de lodo

Focus Question

How can nature be
part of a home?

This house is made of Mud.

We made it, my Brothers and Sisters,
and Mother and Father.

We made this house from Earth, and
Water, and Straw.

We mixed them all together

And together made our Home.

This house is round, like the Earth,
and the Sun, and the Moon.

Esta casa está hecha de Lodo.

La hicimos, mis Hermanos y Hermanas, y Mamá y Papá.

Hicimos esta casa de Tierra, de Agua y de Paja.

Las mezclamos todas juntas y juntos hicimos nuestro Hogar.

Esta casa es redonda, como la Tierra, el Sol y la Luna.

119

It has only one door in and out.

But it has many windows so the breezes can pass through.

At night we can see the Stars,

And during the day, the Sky.

Tiene sólo una puerta para salir y entrar.

Pero tiene muchas ventanas por las cuales atraviesan las brisas.

✳

Por las noches podemos ver las Estrellas

Y durante el día, el Cielo.

We share our house with animals, large and small.

There are bugs that live in our walls.

There are mice that have tiny tunnels under our floor.

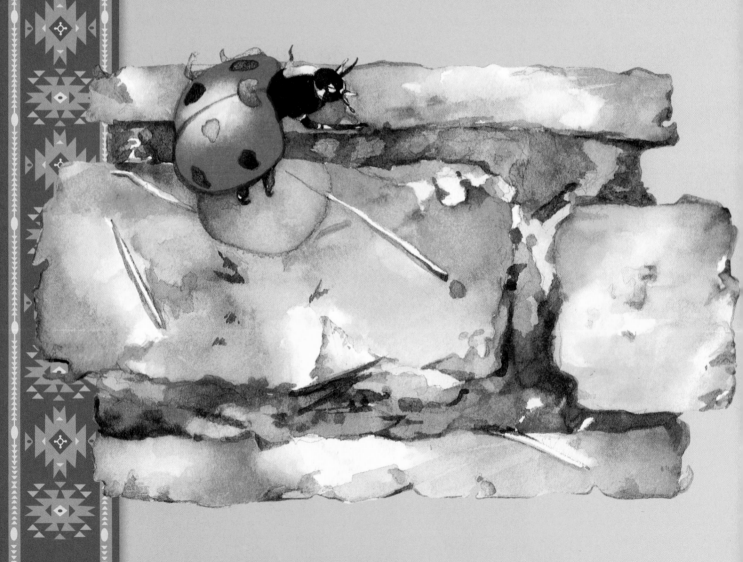

Compartimos nuestra casa con los animales, grandes y pequeños.

Hay bichitos que viven en nuestras paredes.

❋

Hay ratoncitos que tienen pequeños túneles bajo nuestro piso.

123

There is my brother's dog, my sister's cat, my mother's bird, and baby brother's black snake.

He's only out at night, when we are asleep, and the mice are awake.

This house has a yard. It is round, too. We call it the Desert.

Hay, el perro de mi hermano, el gato de mi hermana, el pájaro de mi mamá y la culebra negra de mi hermanito.

La culebra sólo sale de noche, cuando estamos dormidos y los ratones están despiertos.

※

Esta casa tiene un jardín. También es redondo.

Lo llamamos el Desierto.

It has a fence around it. The fence is called the Mountains.

✳

Our yard, and our fence, are covered with plants—

From the giant cacti, to the smallest blades of grass.

Alrededor tiene una corralada. La corralada se llama las Montañas.

Nuestro jardín y nuestro muro, están cubiertos de plantas—

Desde el gigante cacto, hasta la hierba más pequeña.

127

Everyone has a name, but they are all called Friends, because they share our yard.

We get many visitors to our house.

✳

The Sun comes every day.

The Wind comes, but never stays.

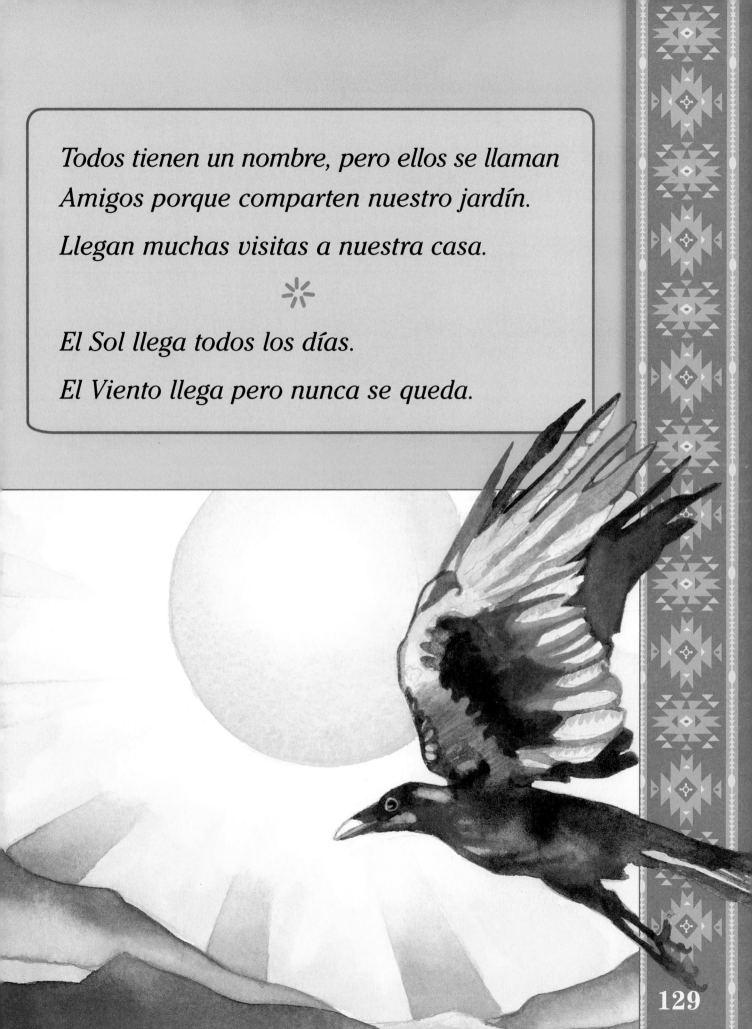

Todos tienen un nombre, pero ellos se llaman
Amigos porque comparten nuestro jardín.

Llegan muchas visitas a nuestra casa.

❉

El Sol llega todos los días.

El Viento llega pero nunca se queda.

129

The Rain's visit is not for long, just long enough for everyone to get a good drink.

La visita de la Lluvia no dura mucho,
sólo lo suficiente para que todos beban
un buen trago.

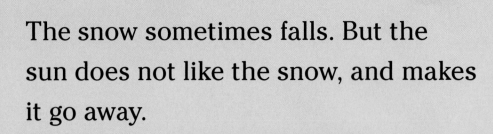

The snow sometimes falls. But the sun does not like the snow, and makes it go away.

This house was made of mud by our family. Made from the same thing our Earth is made of.

La nieve a veces cae. Pero al sol no le gusta la nieve y la hace que se vaya.

Esta casa fue hecha de lodo por nuestra familia. Hecha de la misma cosa de lo que está hecha nuestra Tierra.

Our house is shared by many, and many come to visit. They are all our Friends.

This house is our Home. And our home is made of Love.

Muchos comparten nuestra casa y muchos vienen a visitar. Todos son nuestros Amigos.

Esta casa es nuestro Hogar. Y nuestro hogar está hecho de Amor.

Meet the Author

Ken Buchanan

Ken Buchanan always dreamed of becoming an author. After many years of hard work, his dream finally came true. After Buchanan wrote this story, he and his family lived in their own mud house in the desert!

Meet the Illustrator

Libba Tracy

Libba Tracy has been a painter and an illustrator for a long time. Tracy gets ideas for her paintings by looking out her window, where she can see the mountains and the desert.

Home, Sweet Home
Theme Connections

Within the Selection

1. What material is the house made of?

2. Who are some of the visitors that live in the house?

Across Selections

3. How are the animals in "This House Is Made of Mud" similar to the animals in "Finding Shelter"?

Beyond the Selection

4. What makes a home special?

Write about It!

Pretend you are building a house. What material will you use?

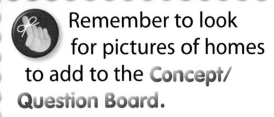

Remember to look for pictures of homes to add to the **Concept/ Question Board.**

A Home for Everyone

by Joan Taylor

Last week local kids helped build a house for their community. The house was for a family that did not have a home.

"Houses cost lots of money. We share the responsibility," said Rico. Rico's class sold fruit bars at sports games. "We made $900!" said Rico.

The money bought two doors for the house. Other kids earned money too. They washed cars. They pet sat. The kids thought about others. They knew people needed homes.

Some classes bought paint. Others bought shingles.

On Saturday the house was completed. It was good and sturdy.

Genre

Newspaper Articles tell about people, places, and things that happen in nations, states, and cities.

Feature

Bylines tell who wrote the article.

1. Where do you find the byline?
   How does it help you?

2. How do the children get money to
   build the house?

3. Think about ways your class could
   earn money. Make a list.

Try It!

Look at different newspapers.
Highlight or circle the byline.

139

Test
Prep

FLORIDA

Test-Taking Strategy: Considering Every Answer Choice

· · · · · · · · · · · · · · · ·

Be sure to read all the answers to a question. You will not know whether an answer is correct unless you read it.

Considering Every Answer Choice

When you take a test, it is important that you carefully read every answer. Think about what the question is asking. Choose the answer that best answers the question.

Listen carefully to this question. Be sure to read all the answer choices.

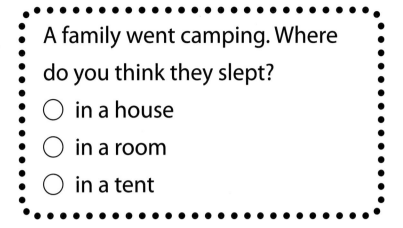

A family went camping. Where do you think they slept?

○ in a house

○ in a room

○ in a tent

The important words in the question are *camping* and *slept.* You have to read all the answer choices to find the one that best answers the question. You can sleep in a house or in a room, but if you are camping, you will probably sleep in a tent.

The third answer is correct. Find the third answer, and point to the circle next to it.

STOP

Test-Taking Practice

Read the story below. Then complete the test on the next page.

Test Tip

Listen carefully to your teacher.

A Strange Home

The sunfish has a strange home. It is a hole in the bottom of a lake. The sunfish swims back and forth to make the hole. It has to do this many times.

The sunfish lays eggs in the hole. It protects the eggs. When they hatch, the babies stay near the hole. When they get big, they swim away.

Complete the test below.

1. What is the home of a sunfish?

○ rock

○ log

○ hole

2. How does the sunfish make its home?

○ by swimming back and forth

○ by digging with its fins

○ by using a tiny stick

3. Where do the baby sunfish stay?

○ in the weeds

○ near their home

○ in the sand

Test Tips

Read the question carefully.

Read each answer choice.

STOP

10

I Am Brave

Everyone is afraid of something. It is okay to have fears. Sometimes fears keep you safe. Sometimes you must face your fears.

Theme Connection

Look at the illustration. How do you think the boy in the illustration feels? How would you feel if you were on stage? Why would you feel that way? What could you do to face your fears?

BIG
Idea

Why is it important
to face some fears?

145

Read the article to find the meanings of these words, which are also in "My Brother Is Afraid of Just About Everything":

✦ underneath
✦ beards
✦ clenched
✦ trembling

Vocabulary Strategy

Apposition can help you find the meaning of *underneath.*

Vocabulary

Warm-Up

Joe wanted to go scuba diving. He loved the ocean. He wanted to see fish from underneath, or below, the surface of the water.

"Mom thinks I'm too young to scuba dive," said Joe.

Joe's uncles laughed. They rubbed the beards on their faces.

Joe clenched his fists. He was tough. He could scuba dive in the ocean.

"The ocean is an exciting place," said one uncle.

Joe's other uncle pretended to dive into the pool in Joe's yard. "Let's teach Joe here!" he said.

Then Joe understood. He could learn to dive in his pool this year.

Joe dived into the cold water. He was trembling when he got out. Joe was happy. His mom was happy too. Joe would be a safe diver.

GAME

Opposite Game Play an opposite game. Read each sentence that contains a selection vocabulary word. Then make up a sentence that means the exact opposite. Example: Joe *relaxed* his hands.

Concept Vocabulary

The concept word for this lesson is **nervous.** To be nervous is to be easily upset or uneasy. Talk about what might make some people nervous. Do you think Joe's mom is nervous? Why?

Genre

Realistic Fiction is a make-believe story that could happen in the real world.

Comprehension Skill

 **Drawing Conclusions**

As you read, use what you learn about the characters and events to help you better understand the selection.

My Brother Is AFRAID

# of Just About EVERYTHING

by Lois Osborn

illustrated by

Erica Pelton Villnave

Focus Question

How could you help a friend overcome his or her fear?

My little brother is afraid of just about everything. Whenever there's a thunderstorm, I know where to find him.

Underneath the bed.

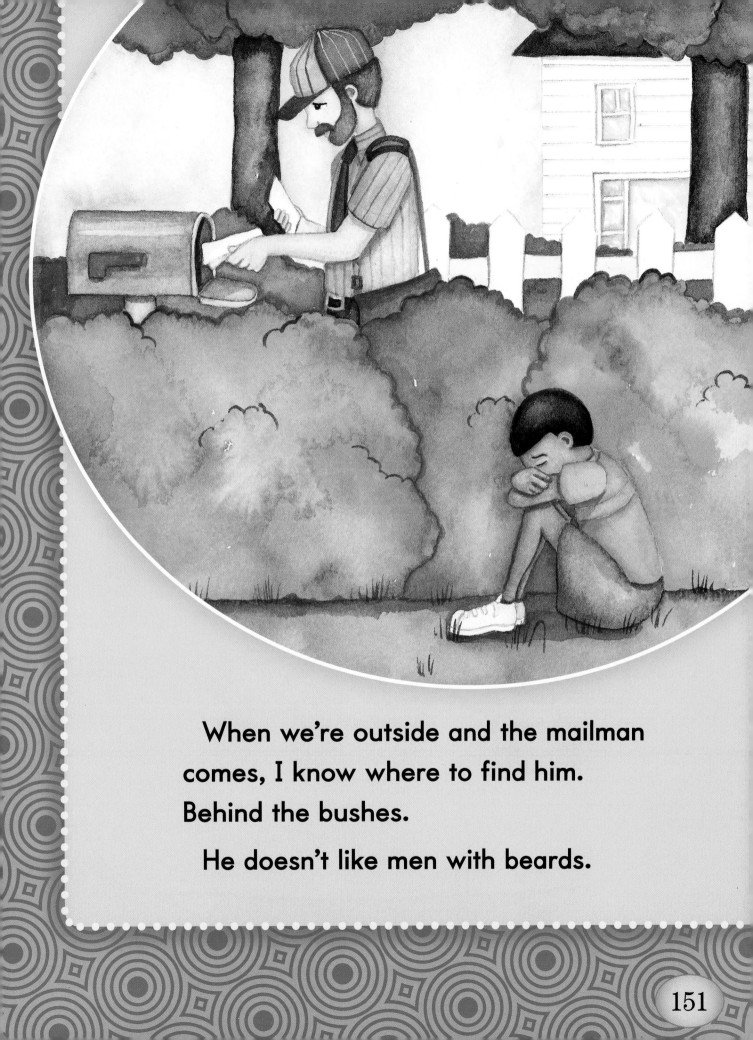

When we're outside and the mailman
comes, I know where to find him.
Behind the bushes.

He doesn't like men with beards.

When he's in the bathtub, he screams if I let the water out. Maybe he thinks he'll go down the drain along with the water.

So I take him out first. Then I empty the tub.

Yesterday my mother started to
vacuum. My brother started to howl.

Maybe he thinks the vacuum cleaner
is a monster. He sure acts that way.
So my mother asked me to take him
for a walk.

We went past my school. "See?" I
said. "That's where you'll be going in
a couple of years."

I could tell by my brother's face
what he thought about *that.*

155

We met some of my friends at the playground. They think my brother is cute. "What's your name?" and "How old are you?" they asked.

Did my brother answer them?
No-o-o, of course not.

He just buried his face in my
stomach, the way he always does.

On our way home, we came to some
railroad tracks. A train was coming, so
we waited to cross.

Most kids think trains are pretty
exciting. They wave at the engineer.
They count cars. But not my brother.

His arms went around me like boa
constrictors. I couldn't have shaken
him loose if I'd wanted to.

Back home, we sat together under the big tree in our backyard. I decided it was time we had a talk.

"Look," I said to him, "did thunder and lightning ever hurt you?" He shook his head.

"Or the mailman, or the vacuum cleaner?" He shook his head again.

"Then how come you're so scared of everything?" I asked.

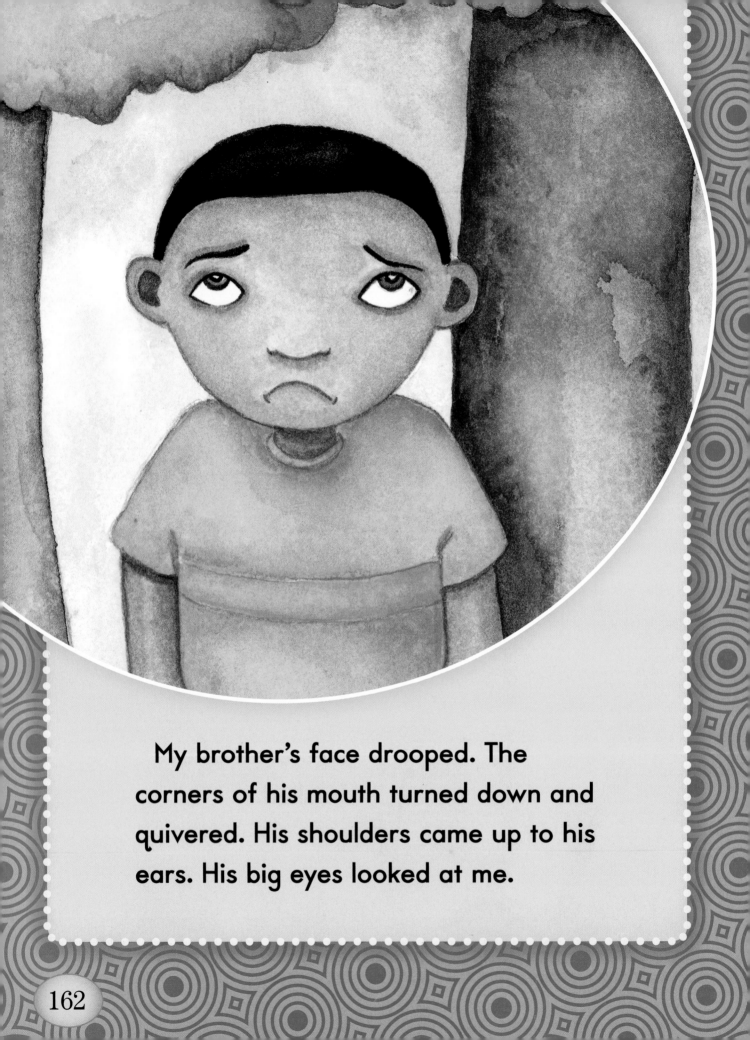

My brother's face drooped. The corners of his mouth turned down and quivered. His shoulders came up to his ears. His big eyes looked at me.

I felt like patting him on the back and saying that everything was okay.

But instead I said, "Look, you've got to get tough. It's stupid to keep on being afraid of things that won't hurt you."

Then I saw a great big, happy smile spread across my brother's face. He was looking at something behind me. I didn't even have to ask what it was.

Nothing else could make my brother
look that happy. It had to be—a dog!

I tried. I tried very hard.

I shut my eyes and pretended the dog wasn't there.

I took deep breaths so my heart wouldn't beat so fast.

I clenched my hands so they would stop trembling.

I prayed the dog would go away.

Then I felt its feet upon my shoulders. I thought of sharp claws.

I felt its rough, wet tongue against the back of my neck. I thought of all those teeth.

That did it!

I couldn't get into the house fast enough! Across the yard I ran. I yanked open the screen door and quickly slammed it shut. I even hooked it.

Safe behind the door, I stood, catching my breath.

Then I went to the window. I knew what I would see.

Yes, there was my brother, with his arms around that dog.

I watched them play together.
I watched them for a long time.

I suppose that dog would have played with me, too, if I had been outside.

But I stayed inside.

I felt bad about it, but I stayed inside.

Oh well, everybody's afraid of something, I guess.

Meet the Author

Lois Osborn

For twenty-six years, Lois Osborn was a teacher. She started writing after she retired. She used to visit schools to read her books and talk about writing.

Meet the Illustrator

Erica Pelton Villnave

Inspiring children to read is a passion for Erica Pelton Villnave. She tries to create characters children can relate to. Villnave often uses watercolors to create her illustrations.

I Am Brave

Theme Connections

Within the Selection

1. Why does the girl ask her brother if the vacuum cleaner has ever hurt him?

2. Why does the girl stay inside when her brother is playing with the dog?

Beyond the Selection

3. What things scare people?

4. How are people brave?

Write about It!

Write a story about a time when someone was brave. The story could be about you.

Remember to look for articles or stories about people being brave to add to the **Concept/Question Board.**

A Trip to the Ocean

Take a Deep Look

The ocean is an exciting place. Some people scuba dive. They go deep underneath the surface of the water. They see lots of fish and plants.

Just Below

Other people snorkel. They put masks on their faces. They look into the water. They don't go deep.

The ocean can seem scary. There are many things to do near the ocean.

At the Beach

Some people collect shells. Others build sand castles. The boy in the picture thinks it is great fun to wade.

Think Link

1. Make a list of fun activities that can be done by the ocean or in the ocean.

2. Tell why an activity from your list might seem scary to someone else.

3. Explain what can be done to make this activity safe and fun instead of scary.

Try It!

Look for more ways to be safe and to have fun at the ocean.

175

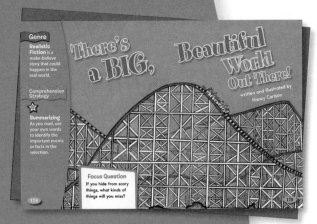

Genre

Realistic Fiction is a make-believe story that could happen in the real world.

Comprehension Strategy

⭐ **Summarizing**
As you read, use your own words to identify the important events or facts in the selection.

There's a BIG, Beautiful World Out There!

written and illustrated by
Nancy Carlson

178

Focus Question
If you hide from scary things, what kinds of things will you miss?

Read the article to find the meanings of these words, which are also in "There's a Big, Beautiful World Out There!" and "Night Comes":

✦ solo
✦ thrill
✦ peeking
✦ sneaking

Vocabulary Strategy

Context Clues help you find the meanings of *peeking* and *sneaking*.

Vocabulary

Warm-Up

Em was getting ready for her concert. "La la la," she sang. Em's mother smiled.

"You love to sing!" said Em's mother.

"I do!" Em sang back.

"My school had concerts when I was your age too," Em's mother said.

"What did you do?" asked Em.

"I played the piano," her mother replied.

176

Em loved to hear her mother play. She thought about what her mother had said.

"I'm singing a solo at the concert," said Em. "Will you play the piano for me?"

"That would thrill me!" smiled Em's mother.

At the concert Em was peeking around the curtain. Em did not see her mother. She saw her mother sneaking backstage to get ready for the concert.

GAME

Fill the Blank Create multiple sentences using blanks instead of the vocabulary words. Have another student fill each blank with the correct word.

Concept Vocabulary

The concept word for this lesson is *universe*. The universe is the sky, the stars, and everything in the world. You are a part of this universe. Explain what you can do to learn more about our universe.

There's a BIG,

Focus Question

If you hide from scary things, what kinds of things will you miss?

Beautiful World Out There!

written and illustrated by
Nancy Carlson

There's a lot to be scared of, that's for sure!

180

There's that mean-looking dog,
and booming thunderstorms.

181

There are roller coasters,
and scary stories in the news.

182

There's a lot to be scared of, like getting up in front of a whole bunch of people, and spiders and other creepy crawly things.

There are clowns, and spooky shadows in your room, and people who look different from you.

All this scary stuff can make you
want to hide under your covers and
never come out.

But after a while, hiding under your covers can get pretty boring.

Maybe that scary dog only looks mean.

If you hide under your covers, you won't see the rainbow after the storm,

and you might never enjoy the thrill of
the ride!

If you hide under your covers, you'll miss your mother saying everything is going to be all right,

and you might never know how
great you sound singing a solo.

If you hide under your covers, you might not see all the interesting things in your own backyard.

You'll miss laughing out loud, and
you won't see the stars come out.

And just think of all the new friends
you'll never meet!

There's a lot to be scared of, but there's
even more to look forward to. . . .

So throw off those covers!

There's a big, beautiful world out there

just waiting for you!

Nancy Carlson

Everyone should have fun, especially children. That is why Nancy Carlson's books are so much fun for children to read. Many of her stories are about important things that happened to her when she was young. She hopes that by writing and drawing about her challenges, children will understand they do not have to be perfect. Carlson likes to remember her favorite kind of book from her childhood as she creates illustrations for her books. If you guessed she liked comic books the best, then you were right!

Theme Connections

Within the Selection

1. What will you miss if you hide under your covers after a storm?

2. What interesting things are shown in the illustration of the backyard?

Across Selections

3. How is this selection like "My Brother Is Afraid of Just About Everything"?

Beyond the Selection

4. What makes you want to hide?

Write about It!

Describe something exciting you would miss if you hid under your covers.

Remember to look for stories about people being brave to add to the **Concept/Question Board.**

Focus Question

Why are some people afraid of the night?

Night Comes

by Beatrice Schenk de Regniers
illustrated by Emma Shaw-Smith

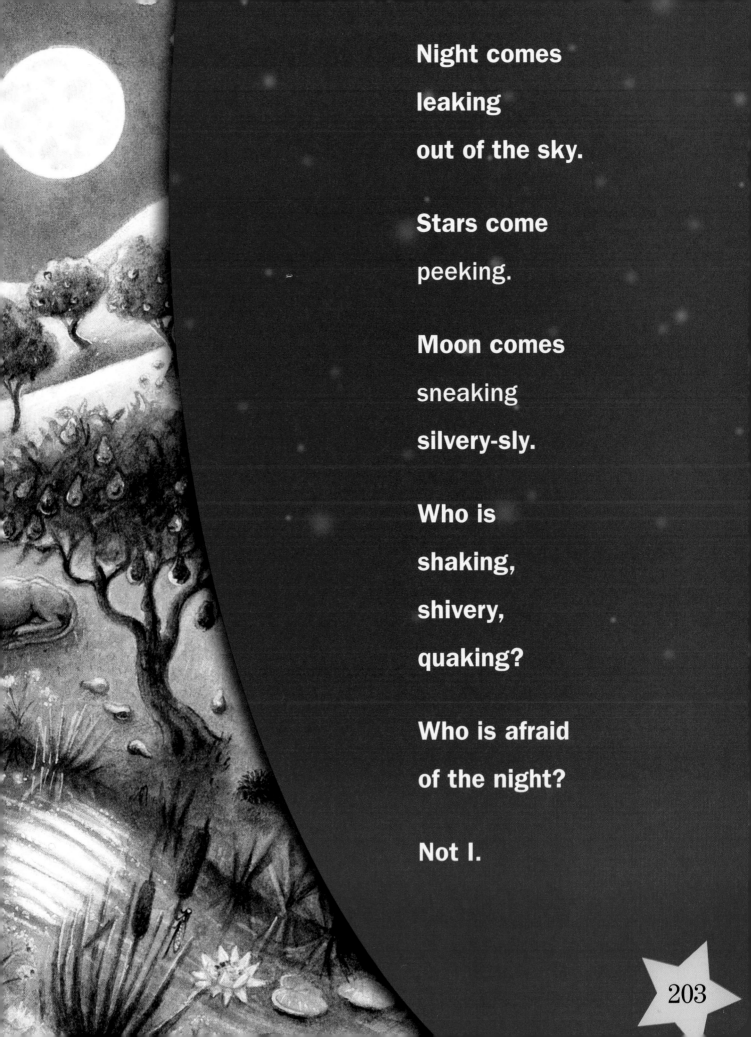

Night comes

leaking

out of the sky.

Stars come

peeking.

Moon comes

sneaking

silvery-sly.

Who is

shaking,

shivery,

quaking?

Who is afraid

of the night?

Not I.

203

World Festival

Lucia is my friend. We go to the World Festival every year. We see customs from around the globe.

First we like to look at the clothes. We look at the kilts of Scotland. We also look at Kangas from Kenya. Kangas can be used as shawls. We choose our favorites. Then we try different foods. My favorite is nut soup. Lucia likes milk pie. Next we listen to music. Polka bands are our favorite. After that we try to do the dances. It is hard to learn the dances of so many cultures. It is great! What a thrill!

It is a long day! We learn about many cultures. We always have fun!

Think Link

1. What is the sequence of events at the World Festival?

2. Why do you think it might be hard to learn the dances?

3. Why do you think attending a World Festival would be fun?

Try It!

Visit the library to find books about other cultures.

Genre

A **fantasy** is a make-believe story that could not happen in the real world.

Comprehension Strategy

⭐ **Clarifying**
As you read, check to make sure you understand what you are reading, and, then clarify any difficult words or phrases.

Clyde Monster

by Robert L. Crowe
illustrated by Kay Chorao

Focus Questions
What fears have you tried to get over? How did you do it?

208   209

Read the article to find the meanings of these words, which are also in "Clyde Monster" and "The Cat and the Mice":

✦ usually
✦ excitement
✦ suggest
✦ clumsy

Vocabulary Strategy

Apposition can help you find the meaning of *suggest.*

Vocabulary

Warm-Up

Mrs. Jones usually had clever, or very smart, students in class. They wanted to start a class newspaper.

"I know there is excitement!" exclaimed Mrs. Jones. "Let me suggest, or give, some ideas. Make a list of jobs. Write who wants to do each job. Write ideas for stories."

The students had a lot to think about. They started to

206

worry. They could not be clumsy about this. But Mrs. Jones wasn't bothered. She refused to think bad thoughts. She could only smile. "Use the ideas I gave you. You won't have any trouble," pointed out Mrs. Jones.

The class worked together. The list they wrote helped. Everyone had a job. They had lots of news to share!

GAME

Guessing Game With a partner, play a guessing game. Use vocabulary words and their definitions. Ask your partner which word means "joy." If your partner guesses *excitement,* then he or she gets to choose a word for you to guess. Play the game until you have reviewed all vocabulary words.

Concept Vocabulary

The concept word for this lesson is *worry.* To worry is to feel uneasy or upset.

Some people worry when they are late. Other people worry when they lose something. Talk about what makes you worry. Do you think everyone worries? Explain why.

Genre

A **fantasy** is a make-believe story that could not happen in the real world.

Comprehension Strategy

 Reality and Fantasy

As you read, decide whether the characters and events are real or make-believe.

208

Clyde Monster

by Robert L. Crowe
illustrated by Kay Chorao

Focus Questions

What fears have you tried to get over? How did you do it?

Clyde wasn't very old, but he was growing—uglier every day. He lived in a large forest with his parents.

Father Monster was a big, big monster
and very ugly, which was good. Friends
and family usually make fun of a pretty
monster. Mother Monster was even uglier
and greatly admired. All in all, they were
a picture family—as monsters go.

Clyde lived in a cave. That is, he was
supposed to live in a cave, at night
anyway. During the day, he played in the
forest, doing typical monster things like
breathing fire at the lake to make the
steam rise.

He also did typical Clyde things like turning somersaults that made large holes in the ground, and generally bumping into things. He was more clumsy than the average monster.

At night, Clyde was supposed to go to his cave and sleep. That's when the trouble started. He refused to go to his cave.

"Why?" asked his mother. "Why won't you go to your cave?"

"Because," answered Clyde, "I'm afraid of the dark."

"Afraid," snorted his father until his nose burned. "A monster of mine afraid? What are you afraid of?"

"People," said Clyde. "I'm afraid there are people in there who will get me."

"That's silly," said his father. "Come, I'll show you." He breathed a huge burst of fire that lit up the cave. "There. Did you see any people?"

"No," answered Clyde. "But they may be hiding under a rock and they'll jump out and get me after I'm asleep."

"That is silly," pointed out his mother with her pointed tongue. "There are no people here. Besides, if there were, they wouldn't hurt you."

"They wouldn't?" asked Clyde.

"No," said his mother. "Would you ever hide in the dark under a bed or in a closet to scare a human boy or girl?"

"Of course not!" exclaimed Clyde, upset that his mother would even think of such a thing.

"Well, people won't hide and scare you either. A long time ago monsters and people made a deal," explained his father. "Monsters don't scare people, and people don't scare monsters."

"Are you sure?" Clyde asked.

"Absolutely," said his mother. "Do you know of a monster who was ever frightened by a people?"

"No," answered Clyde after some thought.

"Do you know of any boys or girls who were ever frightened by a monster?"

"No," he answered quickly.

"There!" said his mother. "Now off to bed."

"And no more nonsense about being scared by people," ordered his father.

"Okay," said Clyde as he stumbled into
the cave. "But could you leave the rock
open just a little?"

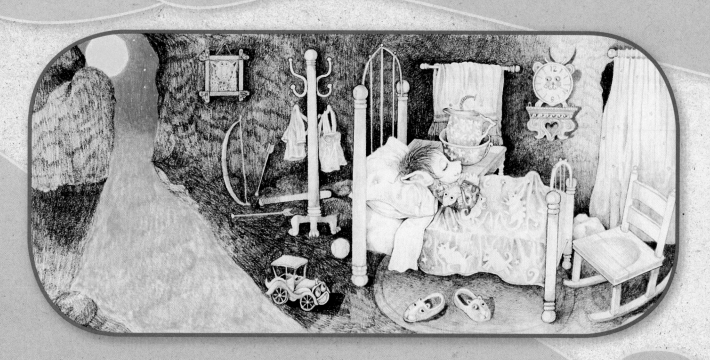

Meet the Author

Robert L. Crowe

School and children were familiar to Robert Crowe. Crowe used to be a teacher. Then he became a superintendent of schools. He wrote "Clyde Monster" to help his own children overcome their fear of the dark.

Meet the Illustrator

Kay Chorao

As a child, Kay Chorao loved to draw. As soon as she was old enough to hold a crayon, she "scribbled drawings over every surface," including the breakfast room table! Chorao is from Indiana. Now she lives in New York City.

Theme Connections

Within the Selection

1. What is surprising about Clyde's fears?

2. How do you know that Clyde is still a little afraid at the end of the story?

Across Selections

3. How is "Clyde Monster" different from the poem "Night Comes"?

Beyond the Selection

4. How has another person helped you face your fears?

Write about It!

Write words that describe how you feel when you are afraid.

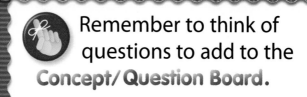

Remember to think of questions to add to the **Concept/Question Board.**

Genre

A **fable** is a short story that teaches a lesson or moral.

Comprehension Strategy

☆ **Predicting** As you read, think about what will happen next in the selection. Confirm your predictions as you continue to read.

Focus Question

Why would a mouse want to stay away from a cat?

The Mice in Council

Aesop
retold by Maria Vasquez
illustrated by Gene Barretta

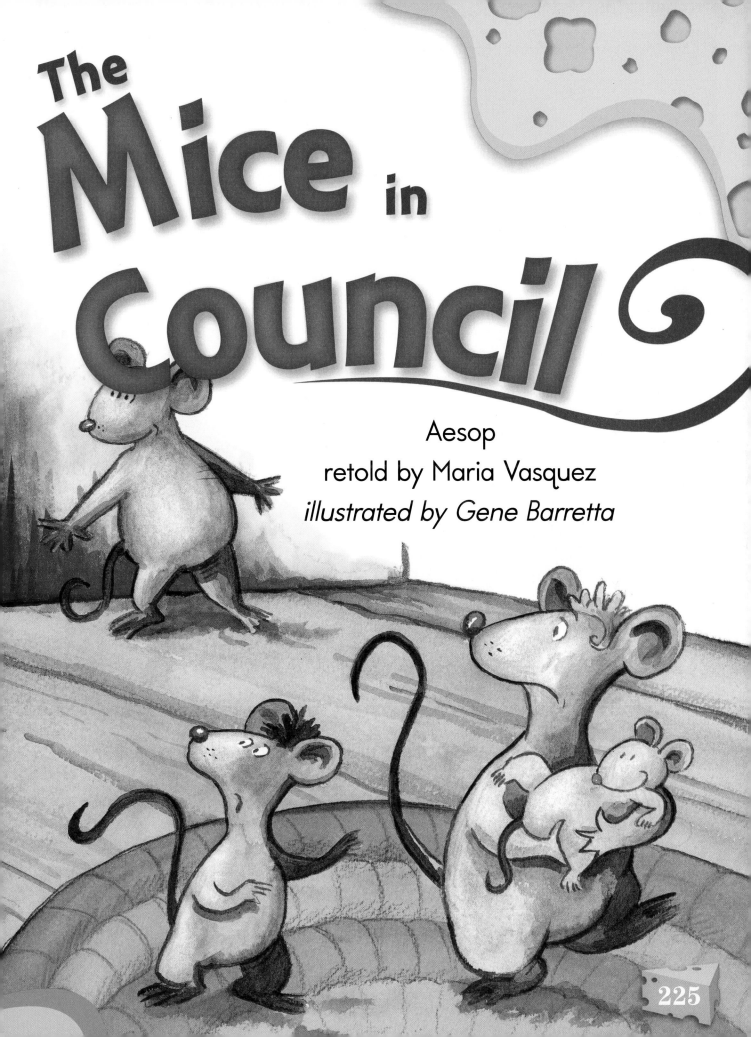

Once, a family of mice lived in a hole in a wall. Usually their days were filled with fun. Sometimes, though, things were not fun.

At times, the cat would appear. It was large and fierce. What a scary sight she was to the poor mice! The mice would have to run from the cat's sharp claws.

The mice called a meeting to suggest ways to stay safe from the cat. Several suggestions were discussed. Finally, a clever mouse yelled, "I think I have it! We can use a bell! We can hang it around the neck of the cat. The sound of the bell will warn us when she is coming near. Then we will have time to run and hide."

The mice squealed loudly. They all agreed upon the idea with excitement.

Then a wise mouse stood up and said, "This is a great idea. But there is one flaw.

Aesop

Aesop was a man who lived more than two thousand years ago. He liked to tell simple stories called fables. Aesop's fables usually have animals as characters and teach the reader a lesson.

Meet the Illustrator

Gene Barretta

Animals that behave like humans are Gene Barretta's favorite things to draw. Barretta enjoys visiting schools to talk to children about his books.

Theme Connections

Within the Selection

1. How would a bell protect the mice?

2. How does fear change the mice's plan?

Across Selections

3. How is the mouse family's fear different from Clyde Monster's fear?

4. How is the fable "The Mice in Council" similar to the story "Clyde Monster"?

Beyond the Selection

5. How can fear protect an animal from its enemies?

Write about It!

Write a few sentences about what the mice could do to avoid the cat. Illustrate it.

Remember to look for pictures of animals or people facing fears to add to the Concept/Question Board.

Science Inquiry

Frozen Fruit Treats

You can make your own frozen treats! Always ask a grown-up for help when working in the kitchen. You might be afraid the recipe won't work. That's okay. If a grown-up helps, things usually turn out. You will need some fruit drink and an ice-cube tray. Then follow these steps:

1. Pour fruit drink into the tray.
2. Put the tray into the freezer.
3. Wait for a few hours or until the fruit punch is frozen.
4. Bend the tray to take out the frozen fruit cubes.

A drink is now a frozen treat!

1. How is the sequence of steps helpful to you?

2. How can a fruit drink become a frozen treat?

3. The recipe says to wait a few hours. Explain why.

Try It!

Try this activity at home with a parent or an adult.

Read the article to find the meanings of these words, which are also in "Ira Sleeps Over":

+ match
+ problem
+ changed mind

234

Vocabulary

Warm-Up

After I won my chess match, my mom said I could go to her office. I can bring my teddy bear, but I'm not going to. I want to look like a grown-up.

Mom has cool things at her office. She has a magnifying glass. It makes my thumb look really big! Mom works with big machines. My dreams used to

be haunted by those big machines. Mom agrees machines can be kind of scary! But she works safely. She wears goggles to keep her eyes safe. And if there is a problem, she can fix it.

I changed my mind. I will bring my teddy bear. I'm not scared—I want my teddy bear to see the cool things my mom does at work.

GAME

Writing a Story Write a story using each of the selection vocabulary words. Think about other things that might be in an office, and include them in your story.

Concept Vocabulary

The concept word for this lesson is *comfort.* Comfort is offered or given when someone is frightened or uneasy. Talk about why all people need comfort at one time or another. Why might comfort be important?

Genre

Realistic Fiction is a make-believe story that could happen in the real world.

Comprehension Skill

☆ **Main Idea and Details**

As you read, identify the main idea and details of the selection.

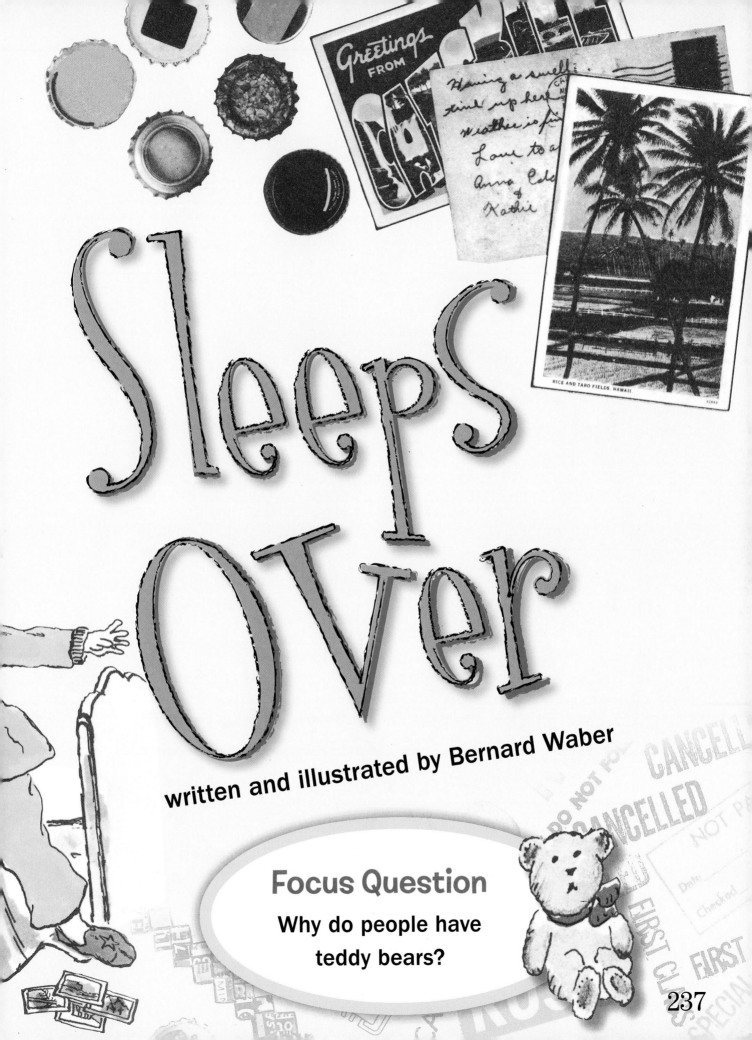

Sleeps Over

written and illustrated by Bernard Waber

Focus Question

Why do people have
teddy bears?

I was invited to sleep at Reggie's
house. Was I happy! I had never slept
at a friend's house before.

But I had a problem. It began when my sister said: "Are you taking your teddy bear along?"

"Taking my teddy bear along!" I said. "To my friend's house? Are you kidding? That's the silliest thing I ever heard! Of course, I'm not taking my teddy bear."

And then she said: "But you never
slept without your teddy bear before.
How will you feel sleeping without
your teddy bear for the very first time?
Hmmmmmmm?"

"I'll feel fine. I'll feel great. I will probably love sleeping without my teddy bear. Just don't worry about it," I said.

"Who's worried?" she said.

But now, she had me thinking about it.
Now, she really had me thinking about it.
I began to wonder: Suppose I won't like
sleeping without my teddy bear. Suppose
I just hate sleeping without my teddy
bear. Should I take him?

"Take him," said my mother.

"Take him," said my father.

"But Reggie will laugh," I said.
"He'll say I'm a baby."

"He won't laugh," said my mother.

"He won't laugh," said my father.

"He'll laugh," said my sister.

I decided not to take my teddy bear.

243

That afternoon, I played with Reggie. Reggie had plans, big plans. "Tonight," he said, "when you come to my house, we are going to have fun, fun, fun. First, I'll show you my junk collection. And after that we'll have a wrestling match. And after that, a pillow fight.

"And after that we'll do magic tricks. And after that we'll play checkers. And after that we'll play dominoes. And after that we can fool around with my magnifying glass."

"Great!" I said. "I can hardly wait. By the way," I asked, "what do you think of teddy bears?"

But Reggie just went on talking and planning as if he had never heard of teddy bears. "And after that," he said, "do you know what we can do after that—I mean when the lights are out and the house is really dark? Guess what we can do?"

"What?" I asked.

"We can tell ghost stories."

"Ghost stories?" I said.

"Ghost stories," said Reggie, "scary, creepy, spooky ghost stories."

I began to think about my teddy bear.

"Does your house get very dark?" I asked.

"Uh-huh," said Reggie.

"Very, very dark?"

"Uh-huh," said Reggie.

"By the way," I said again,
"what do you think of teddy
bears?"

Suddenly, Reggie was in a
big hurry to go someplace.
"See you tonight," he said.

"See you," I said.

I decided to take my teddy bear.

"Good," said my mother.

"Good," said my father.

But my sister said: "What if Reggie wants to know your teddy bear's name. Did you think about that? And did you think about how he will laugh and say Tah Tah is a silly, baby name, even for a teddy bear?"

"He won't ask," I said.

"He'll ask," she said.

I decided not to take my teddy bear.

At last, it was time to go to Reggie's house.

"Good night," said my mother.

"Good night," said my father.

"Sleep tight," said my sister.

I went next door where Reggie lived.

That night, Reggie showed me his junk. He showed me his flashlight, his collection of bottle caps, a chain made of chewing gum wrappers, some picture postcards, an egg timer, jumbo goggles, a false nose and mustache, and a bunch of old rubber stamps and labels from his father's office. We decided to play "office" with the rubber stamps.

After that we had a wrestling match.
And after that we had a pillow fight.
And after that Reggie's father said:
"Bedtime!"

"Already?" said Reggie.

"Already," said his father.

We got into bed.

"Good night," said Reggie's father.

"Good night," we said.

Reggie sighed.

I sighed.

"We can still tell ghost stories," said Reggie.

"Do you know any?" I asked.

"Uh-huh," said Reggie.

Reggie began to tell a ghost story:

"Once there was this ghost and he lived in a haunted house only he did most of the haunting himself. This house was empty except for this ghost because nobody wanted to go near this house, they were so afraid of this ghost.

And every night this ghost would walk
around this house and make all kinds of
clunky, creeky sounds. *Aroomp! Aroomp!*
Like that. And he would go around
looking for people to scare because
that's what he liked most to do: scare
people. And he was very scary to look at.
Oh, was he scary to look at!"

Reggie stopped. "Are you scared?"
he asked.

"Uh-huh," I said. "Are you?"

"What?" said Reggie.

"Are you scared?"

"Just a minute," said Reggie, "I have
to get something."

"What do you have to get?" I asked.

"Oh, something," said Reggie.

258

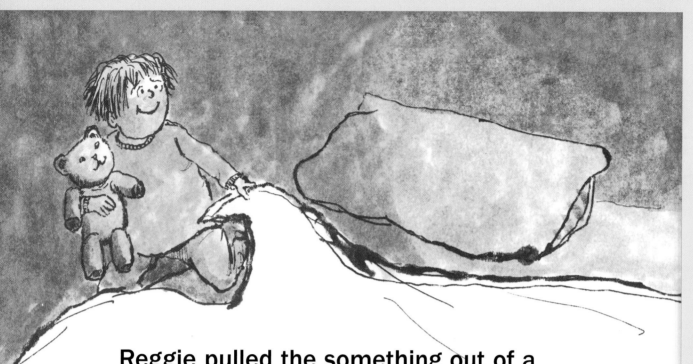

Reggie pulled the something out of a drawer. The room was dark, but I could see it had fuzzy arms and legs and was about the size of a teddy bear. I looked again. It was a teddy bear.

Reggie got back into bed. "Now, about this ghost . . ." he said.

"Is that your teddy bear?" I asked.

"What?" said Reggie.

"Is that your teddy bear?"

"You mean this teddy bear?"

"The one you're holding," I said.

"Uh-huh," Reggie answered.

"Do you sleep with him all of the time?"

"What?" said Reggie.

"Do you sleep with him all of the time?"

"Uh-huh."

"Does your teddy bear have a name? Does your teddy bear have a name?" I said louder.

"Uh-huh," Reggie answered.

"What is it?"

"You won't laugh?" said Reggie.

"No, I won't laugh," I said.

"Promise?"

"I promise."

"It's Foo Foo."

"Did you say 'Foo Foo'?"

"Uh-huh," said Reggie.

"Just a minute," I said, "I have to get something."

"What do you have to get?" Reggie asked.

"Oh, something," I answered.

The next minute, I was ringing my own
doorbell. The door opened.

"Ira!" everyone said. "What are you
doing here?"

"I changed my mind," I answered.

"You what!" said my mother.

"You what!" said my father.

"You what!" said my sister.
(She was still up.)

"I changed my mind," I said. "I decided to take Tah Tah after all."

I went upstairs. Soon, I was down again with Tah Tah.

My sister said: "Reggie will laugh. You'll see how he'll laugh. He's just going to fall down laughing."

"He won't laugh," said my mother.

"He won't laugh," said my father.

"He won't laugh," I said.

I came back to Reggie's room. "I have
a teddy bear, too," I said. "Do you want
to know his name?" I waited for Reggie
to say, Uh-huh. But Reggie didn't say,
Uh-huh. Reggie didn't say anything. I
looked at Reggie. He was fast asleep.
Just like that, he had fallen asleep.

"Reggie! Wake up!" I said. "You have to finish telling the ghost story." But Reggie just held his teddy bear closer and went right on sleeping. And after that—well, there wasn't anything to do after that. "Good night," I whispered to Tah Tah. And I fell asleep, too.

Bernard Waber

Writing about family problems is something Bernard Waber loves to do. Waber uses funny characters to tell about things that might happen to you or me. He is best known for his books about a crocodile named Lyle. Waber's funny illustrations make children and grown-ups laugh out loud!

Theme Connections

Within the Selection

1. Why is Ira worried about taking his teddy bear to Reggie's house?

2. What changes the way Ira feels?

Across Selections

3. How is this story similar to "My Brother Is Afraid of Just About Everything"?

Beyond the Selection

4. How have you helped someone who was afraid?

Write about It!

Write a few sentences about a time when you stayed at a friend's or relative's house.

Remember to look for pictures of people facing fears to add to the Concept/Question Board.

Social Studies Inquiry

What Will You Be?

There are all kinds of jobs. What will you be when you grow up?

Outdoors

Some people like to work outdoors. Mail carriers work outside. Park rangers work outside too.

Builders

Some people like to build. Carpenters build. So do construction workers. They build houses, offices, and even schools.

Animal Lovers

People who work at a zoo or as a vet love animals. They might solve an animal's health problem. Watch people who work in your city. What will you be?

1. How is the heading for the third paragraph helpful?

2. Why might someone who likes to work outside consider a job as a mail carrier?

3. Some people love animals. Explain why the zoo might be a good place for them to work.

Try It!

Watch people working at school or in your community. Write about the jobs you like.

Unit 10

Test Prep
FLORIDA

Test-Taking Strategy: Referring to a Story to Answer Questions

To answer some questions on a test, you will have to read a story. You must use the information in the story to answer the questions.

Referring to a Story to Answer Questions

Sometimes you will read a story on a test. You will have to answer questions about the story. It is important that you use the information in the story to answer the questions.

Listen carefully as this story is read. Follow along, and think about the story as you listen.

Nick is a big brown dog. He has floppy ears. Nick likes to chase a ball. If you throw the ball, he will run after it. Then he will bring it back.

Listen carefully to the question.

What color is Nick?

○ brown

○ gray

○ white

Look back at the story. The first sentence is *Nick is a big brown dog.* This tells you the answer. The story says Nick is a *brown* dog. Find the first answer, and point to the circle next to it.

STOP

Test-Taking Practice

Read the story below. Then complete the test on the next page.

First Ride

"Just ride like you always do," said Dad. "Let's go!"

Kerry was a little afraid. Even so, she started pedaling. Mom was down the street in front of the house. Kerry felt Dad let go of the bike. She did not fall.

Mom was clapping. Kerry kept pedaling. She was doing it! When she got close to Mom, she put on the brakes and stopped.

"Mom, I did it!" Kerry got off the bike and gave Mom a hug. Then Kerry got back on the bike and rode back to Dad.

Complete the test below.

1. Kerry was riding a

◯ wagon.

◯ sled.

◯ bike.

2. Who was clapping?

◯ Mom

◯ Dad

◯ Kerry

3. At the end of the story, Kerry

◯ ran to Mom.

◯ rode back to Dad.

◯ went into the house.

Test Tip

Use the story to answer the questions or complete the sentences.

Test Tips

Read each answer choice. Look back at the story if you are not sure.

STOP

Pronunciation Key

a as in **a**t
ā as in l**a**te
â as in c**a**re
ä as in f**a**ther
e as in s**e**t
ē as in m**e**
i as in **i**t
ī as in k**i**te
o as in **o**x
ō as in r**o**se

ô as in b**o**ught and r**a**w
oi as in c**oi**n
o͝o as in b**oo**k
o͞o as in t**oo**
or as in f**or**m
ou as in **ou**t
u as in **u**p
ū as in **u**se
ûr as in t**ur**n, g**er**m, l**ear**n, f**ir**m, w**or**k

ə as in **a**bout, chick**e**n, penc**i**l, cann**o**n, circ**u**s
ch as in **ch**air
hw as in **wh**ich
ng as in ri**ng**
sh as in **sh**op
th as in **th**in
th as in **th**ere
zh as in trea**s**ure

The mark (′) is placed after a syllable with a heavy accent, as in **chicken** (**chik′** ən).

The mark (′) after a syllable shows a lighter accent, as in **disappear** (**dis′** ə pēr′).

Glossary

A

absolutely (ab´ sə loot´ lē) *adv.* Certainly; without a doubt.

address (ad´ res) *n.* A building number that helps to find a house or business on a street.

area (âr´ ē ə) *n.* Part of a town, city, country, or the world.

at hand (at hand) *adv.* Within reach.

B

beards (bērdz) *n.* Plural of **beard:** The hair that grows on a man's face.

belonging (bi lông´ ing) *v.* To be a member of something, like a club.

bricklayers (brik´ lā´ ərz) *n.* Plural of **bricklayer:** A person who builds walls using bricks or concrete blocks.

builders (bil´ dərz) *n.* Plural of **builder:** A person who builds or makes things, like houses.

bulldozer (bool´ dō´ zər) *n.* A large powerful machine used to move dirt, stones, and trees.

bulldozer

buried (ber´ ēd) *v*. Past tense of **bury:** To hide, cover up.

C

cacti (kak´ tī) *n*. Plural of **cactus:** A desert plant.

cactus

carpenters (kär´ pən tərz) *n*. Plural of **carpenter:** A person who makes things out of wood.

cement (si ment´) *n*. A mix of sand, water, and rock that dries as hard as stone.

changed mind (chānjd mīnd) *v*. Past tense of **change mind:** To go back on a decision.

clay (klā) *n*. Soft, sticky mud.

clenched (klencht) *v*. Past tense of **clench:** To close tightly.

clever (klev´ ər) *adj*. Very smart.

clumsy (klum´ zē) *adj*. Awkward; not graceful.

clumsy

comfort (kum´ fərt) *n.* A good feeling; you have what you need.

creatures (krē´ chərz) *n.* Plural of **creature:** A living person or animal.

D

decided (di sī´ ded) *v.* Past tense of **decide:** To make up your mind.

E

electrician (i lek trish´ ən) *n.* A person who works with wires and electricity.

enemies (en´ ə mēz) *n.* Plural of **enemy:** A person or animal who wants to hurt another.

excitement (ik sīt´ mənt) *n.* A mood or feeling of high interest or energy; delight; joy.

exciting (ik sī´ ting) *adj.* Very interesting.

exclaimed (ik sklāmd´) *v.* Past tense of **exclaim:** To speak out suddenly and loudly.

F

famous (fā´ məs) *adj.* Well known.

feeling (fē´ ling) *n.* An emotion. Sadness, joy, fear, and anger are feelings.

fence (fens) *n.* Something used to border, protect, or surround an area.

fence

floor (flôr) *n.* The area of a room that people walk or stand on.

fold (fōld) *v.* To bend in sections.

G

goggles (gog´ əlz) *n.* Protective glasses.

goggles

H

hibernating (hī´ bər nāt´ ing) *v.* Form of the verb **hibernate:** To sleep through winter.

home (hōm) *n.* A place people live.

hut (hut) *n.* A small plain house.

I

important (im pôr´ tənt) *adj.* Having great value or meaning.

L

leaking (lēk´ ing) *v.* Form of the verb **leak:** To slowly come out.

M

magnifying glass (mag´ nə fī´ ing glas) *n.* A piece of glass that makes things look bigger.

match (mach) *n.* A contest or game.

mud (mud) *n.* Soft, wet, and heavy dirt or earth.

N

nests (nests) *n.* Plural of **nest:** A place built by some animals and birds for laying their eggs or raising their young.

nest

news (nooz) *n.* A report or information on something that just happened.

O

office (ô´ fis) *n.* A place businesspeople work.

Oval Office (ō´ vəl ô´ fis) *n.* A place the president works.

Pronunciation Key: at; l**ā**te; c**â**re; f**ä**ther; s**e**t; m**ē**; **i**t; k**ī**te; **o**x; r**ō**se; **ô** in b**ou**ght; c**oi**n; b**oo**k; t**oo**; f**or**m; **ou**t; **u**p; **ū**se; t**û**rn; **ə** sound in **a**bout, chick**e**n, penc**i**l, cann**o**n, circ**u**s; **ch**air; **hw** in **wh**ich; ri**ng**; **sh**op; **th**in; **th**ere; **zh** in trea**s**ure.

P

packed (pakt) *adj.* Pressed or squeezed together.

peeking (pēk´ing) *v.* Form of the verb **peek:** To look quickly or secretly.

plans (planz) *n.* Plural of **plan:** An idea for doing something that is thought out ahead of time.

plumber (plum´ûr) *n.* A person who fixes and puts together water pipes.

pointed out (poin´ted out) *v.* Past tense of **point out:** To explain.

porch (pôrch) *n.* An entrance covered with a roof.

porch

president (prez´i dənt) *n.* The leader of the United States.

pretended (pri ten´ded) *v.* Past tense of **pretend:** To make believe.

problem (prob´ləm) *n.* A difficulty; a tricky or uncomfortable situation.

protect (prō tekt´) *v.* To keep safe.

pueblo (pweb´ lō) *n*. A group of houses built on top of each other, made of stone or adobe bricks.

pueblo

quaking (kwāk´ ing) *v*. Form of the verb **quake:** To shake or tremble.

R

refused (ri fūzd´) *v*. Past tense of **refuse:** To turn down or say no.

roof (ro͞of) *n*. The outer covering of the top of a house or building.

S

scared (skârd) *v*. Past tense of **scare:** To frighten or become afraid.

shadows (shad´ ōz) *n*. Plural of **shadow:** Area of darkness where there is little or no light.

shadow

shady (shā´ dē) *adj*. Giving shade; blocking out light.

share (shâr) *v*. To divide with others.

281

Pronunciation Key: at; lāte; câre; fäther; set; mē; it; kīte; ox; rōse; ô in bought; coin; boๅok; tōō; form; out; up; ūse; tûrn; ə sound in about, chicken, pencil, cannon, circus; chair; hw in which; ring; shop; thin; there; zh in treasure.

shelter (shel´ tûr) *n.* Something that covers or protects.

shivery (shiv´ ər ē) *adj.* Describes someone who is **shivering:** To shake because of cold or fear.

simple (sim´ pəl) *adj.* Plain.

sneaking (snēk´ ing) *v.* Form of the verb **sneak:** To move or act quietly or secretly.

solo (sō´ lō) *n.* Music that one person sings or plays on an instrument.

spooky (spoๅo´ kē) *adj.* Scary.

squealed (skwēld) *v.* Past tense of **squeal:** To make a loud cry or sound.

sturdy (stûr´ dē) *adj.* Strong.

suggest (səg jest´) *v.* To give or tell an idea.

symbol (sim´ bəl) *n.* A thing that stands for something else.

tarry (târ´ ē) *v.* To delay or wait; to do something slowly.

teddy bear (ted´ ē bâr) *n.* A stuffed toy bear.

teddy bear

thaw (thô) *n.* When the weather becomes warmer in winter and things melt.

thinks (thingks) *v.* Form of the verb **think:** To believe.

thrill (thril) n. A feeling of excitement.

tin (tin) *n.* A kind of metal sometimes used to make cans.

tin

tough (tuf) *adj.* Brave; able to put up with something hard or difficult.

trembling (trem´ bəl ing) *v.* Form of the verb **tremble:** To shake.

trouble (trub´ əl) *n.* Problems; difficulty.

trudge (truj) *v.* To walk slowly with heavy steps.

tunnels (tun´ əlz) *n.* Plural of **tunnel:** An underground passageway.

U

underground (un´ dər ground´) *n.* Below Earth's surface.

underneath (un´ dər nēth´) *adv.* Below.

usually (ū´ zhoo əl ē) *adv.* Most of the time.

Pronunciation Key: at; lāte; câre; fäther; set; mē; it; kīte; ox; rōse; ô in bought; coin; bŏŏk; tŏŏ; form; out; up; ūse; tûrn; ə sound in about, chicken, pencil, cannon, circus; chair; hw in which; ring; shop; thin; there; zh in treasure.

White House (wīt hous) *n.* Where the president of the United States lives.

windows (win´ dōz) *n.* Plural of **window:** An opening in a wall or roof of a house that lets in air and light.

window

wood (wŏŏd) *n.* The hard material that covers the trunk and branches of many plants.

woven (wō´ vən) *v.* Past tense of **weave:** To twist and wind together.

wrestling (res´ ling) *n.* A sport in which two people try to hold each other down with strength.

yard (yärd) *n.* The area of ground around a house, school, or other building.